About the Author

Joyce Horley is a retired housewife living with her husband in Oxfordshire and has two grown up sons and a granddaughter. She has never had a book published before but has written stories all her life.

Lockdown has raised people's awareness of nature generally and birds are frequent visitors to our gardens. She hopes this tale will spark interest in the natural world.

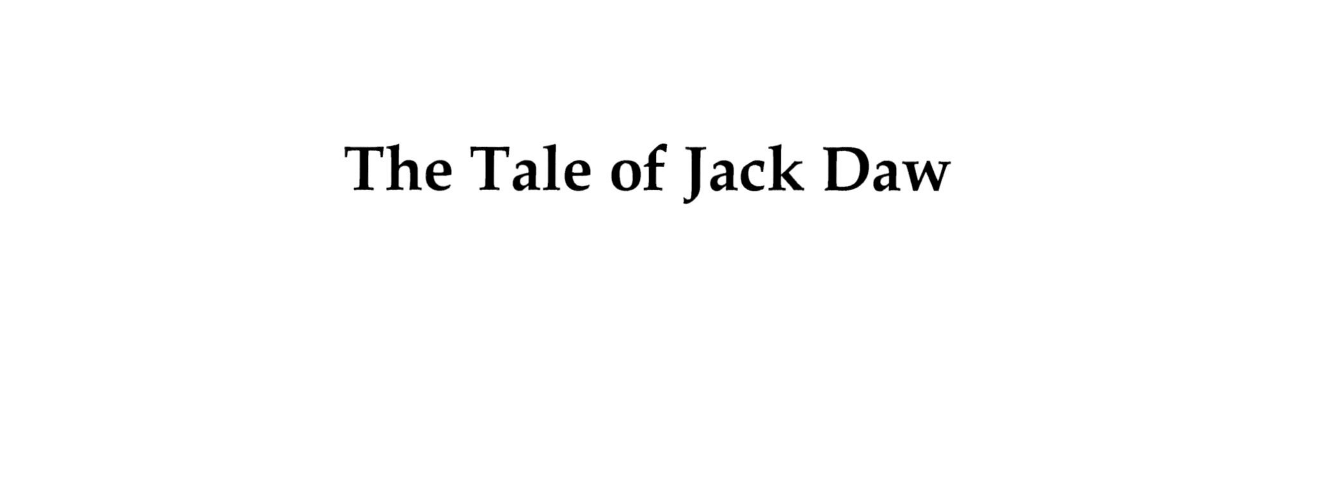

The Tale of Jack Daw

Joyce Horley

The Tale of Jack Daw

Nightingale Books

NIGHTINGALE PAPERBACK

A CIP catalogue record for this title is
available from the British Library.
ISBN 978-1-83875-437-2

Nightingale Books is an imprint of
Pegasus Elliot MacKenzie Publishers Ltd.
www.pegasuspublishers.com

First Published in 2022

Nightingale Books
Sheraton House Castle Park
Cambridge England

Printed & Bound in Great Britain

Dedication

For Holly my granddaughter

It was a sunny spring morning and Jack Daw was perched on a branch of a fir tree on the edge of a wood. He lived there with Jill. Now Jack Daw was a handsome bird with black feathers, a grey head and pearly eyes.

Nearby lived their neighbour, Squawky, a magnificent magpie with black and white feathers and a long glossy green tail. Squawky was interested in Jack and Jill Daw and watched their every move.

Jack and Jill Daw were building a nest not far from the woodland in a chimney in Mr. Green's farmhouse. For days now they had been collecting sticks, all the same length, and carefully dropping them down the chimney, slowly building it to the right height.

Squawky watched their every move.

One morning Squawky followed Jack to a field full of sheep. He was flying low along the barbed wire fence pecking at the lumps of sheep's wool that had got caught up in it. *I know what that's for,* thought Squawky. It is to line the nest. Jill is still nest building but when it is all finished she will sit on her eggs until the baby chicks hatch. Last year Squawky had seen their eggs, pale blue with dark speckles. Squawky was very interested in Jack and Jill's nest building and watched their every move.

I must make a plan

The trouble was that Squawky rather liked to eat baby birds. Last year Jack Daw and Jill never left the nest unattended. *I wonder how I can I get them away from the nest this year,* thought Squawky. *I have to make a plan.*

So Squawky watched their every move.

Jack is very attracted to shiny objects and had collected some sparkling jewellery, which Jill had placed around the nest. *It would be lovely to find something really special this year,* thought Jack. So Jack flew off high into the sky over hills towards the hotel in the village. On occasions he had noticed open windows and had flown down to sit on the sills and peer in.

Sometimes there had been jewellery on the dressing tables and he wondered if there might be something today. Hurrah! A diamond sparkling ring. Jill would love it and the sun would make it glow. Just then a lady came into the room and shut the window. He would have to try again later.

Jill had started to sit on the nest in the chimney for long periods and Jack, being bored with sitting on the chimney pot, made more and more flights towards the village. And of course Squawky followed but kept his distance. From afar he could see Jack peering into a window of the hotel. Goodness he had disappeared into the room only to fly out again seconds later with something sparkling in his beak. What had he found? Whatever it was, it must have been something special because Jack did a loop the loop in the sky before returning to the nest.

Squawky was very interested and watched Jack's every move.

Jill was so happy with the ring that she placed it amongst the twigs to catch the spring sunshine. It was not long after that her five pale blue eggs with dark speckles began to hatch. Not all at the same time but a few days apart. Jack was working very hard flying to and fro with food for the chicks. But Jack and Jill never left the nest together. Squawky was being a nuisance always fluttering around.

He was very interested and watched every move.

A week later Squawky decided to put his plan into action. Somehow he must get to the nest and steal the sparkling object while Jack was away collecting food for the chicks. While Squawky was watching the chimney pot the farm cat appeared from behind it. Immediately Jill flew off the nest to scare away the cat, making a terrible shrieking noise. Squawky saw his chance and grabbed the ring. There was no time for a chick as the cat was leaping around the roof. Frightened by the noise the cat ran off. Jill went back to the nest and Squawky flew off with the ring in his beak.

The next day, having heard from Jill about the cat and the disappearing ring, Jack decided to stay nearby to keep a close eye on the nest. Squawky waited for Jack to go hunting. Now was his chance for a fat juicy chick. He picked up the ring, flew to the chimney pot putting his head into the chimney with the ring in his beak. Jill immediately flew up and tried to grab the ring making a terrible noise, so much so that Squawky, distracted, dropped the ring. Jack Daw hearing Jill’s cries came to the rescue saving both the chicks and the ring.

From then onwards Jill never left the nest until their chicks fledged and for the time being Squawky left them in peace but he was still very interested in what they did and watched their every move.